Other books by Exley:
Cat Quotations   Cats a Celebration
The Fanatics Guide to Cats   The World's Greatest Cat Cartoons
The Crazy World of Cats   Cats (and other Crazy Cuddlies)
An Illustrated Cat Lover's Notebook

Published simultaneously in 1993 by Exley Publications in Great
Britain, and Exley Giftbooks in the USA.
Second edition 1994.

Edited by Helen Exley
Border illustrations by Bridgit Flinn

Copyright © Helen Exley 1993.
ISBN 1-85015-425-2

Pictures selected by Helen Exley.
Designed by Pinpoint Design.
Picture research by P. A. Goldberg and J. Clift/Image Select, London.
Typeset by Delta, Watford.
Printed and bound by Grafo, S.A., Bilbao, Spain.

Exley Publications Ltd, 16 Chalk Hill, Watford, Herts WD1 4BN,
United Kingdom.
Exley Giftbooks, 232 Madison Avenue, Suite 1206, New York,
NY 10016, USA.
Picture credits: Fine Art Photographic Library: cover; Maria Teresa
Meloni: title page; Archiv Fur Kunst, Berlin: page 39; Bridgeman
Art Library, London: page 51, 57; Chris Beetles Gallery, London:
pages 8, 24, 32, 34; © Dede Moser, Switzerland: pages 20, 42, 54;
© Ditz "Old Mr Tombs": page 53; Explorer, Paris: page 44; Fine Art
Photographic Library: pages 14, 19, 30, 60; Giraudon, Paris: page
13; Images/Horizon Picture Library and © John Wilkinson: pages
22, 37; © Lesley Fotherby: page 6.

CAT
· *Lovers* ·
ADDRESS BOOK

EDITED BY HELEN EXLEY

EXLEY
NEW YORK · WATFORD, UK

_____

_____

_____

_____

_____

_____

_____

_____

_____

_____

_____

_____

_____

_____

If you are worthy of its affection, a cat will be your friend,
but never your slave.

THEOPHILE GAUTIER

A cat sees no good reason why it should obey another
animal, even if it does stand on two legs.

SARAH THOMPSON

B

B

_Cats are kindly masters, just so long as you
remember your place._

PAUL GRAY

Lait pur *de la Vingeanne*
Stérilisé

Guillot frères
Montigny sur Vingeanne
Côte d'Or

steinlen

A cat allows you to sleep on the bed. On the edge.

JENNY DE VRIES

C

_____

_____

_____

_____

_____

_____

_____

_____

Humans have remade dogs to suit their own ends. Cats are exactly the same as they were ten thousand years ago.

MARION C. GARRETTY, B.1917

_____

_____

_____

_____

Cat: a pygmy lion who loves mice, hates dogs, and patronizes human beings.

OLIVER HERFORD

G

H

_Cats were put into the world to disprove the dogma that all
things were created to serve man._

PAUL GRAY

A kitten is the delight of a household. All day long a comedy is played out by an incomparable actor.

CHAMPFLEURY (1821-1899)

L

Dogs come when they are called; cats take a message
and get back to you.

MARY BLY

_____

_____

_____

_____

_____

_____

_____

M

M

M

_____

_____

_____

_____

_____

_____

_____

Dessins sans paroles

des Chats

par

Steinlen

PARIS
ERNEST FLAMMARION
EDITEUR
26 Rue Racine

Dogs live with you, cats board with you.

PAM BROWN, B.1928

R

R

S

The smallest feline is a masterpiece.

LEONARDO DA VINCI

*I don't mind a cat, in its place. But its place is not in the
middle of my back at 4 a.m.*

MAYNARD GOOD STODDARD

*One small cat changes coming home to an empty house
to coming home.*

PAM BROWN, B.1928

_____

_____

_____

_____

_____

_____

_____

_____

_____

_____

_____

_____

_____

_____

_____

_____

_____

_____

Cats cannot be made to do anything useful.

P.J. O'ROURKE

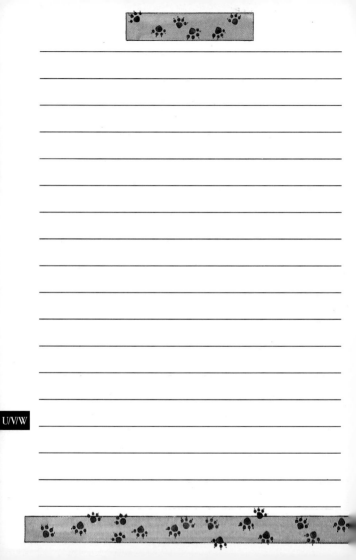

U/V/W

There is nothing so lowering to one's self-esteem as the
affectionate contempt of a beloved cat.

MONICA EDWARDS